Boosey + Hawkes

$3.00
A/C

"The Little Sweep"

(LET'S MAKE AN OPERA)

BENJAMIN BRITTEN

BOOSEY AND HAWKES

Benjamin Britten

The Little Sweep

The Opera from

"Let's Make An Opera"

An Entertainment for Young People

Libretto
by
Eric Crozier

Vocal Score for Piano Duet
by Arthur Oldham

Price 12/6 *net*

Hawkes & Son
(London) Limited
Sole Selling Agents:
Boosey & Hawkes, Ltd.
295 Regent Street, London, W.1
New York · Chicago · Los Angeles · Paris
Buenos Aires · Toronto · Capetown · Sydney · Bonn

The cover is from a ceramic entitled
"The Little Sweep" by Ralph Wood, by kind permission
of the Victoria and Albert Museum (Crown Copyright).

Printed in England

B. & H. 16895

Affectionately dedicated to the real Gay, Juliet, Sophie, Tina, Hughie, Jonny and Sammy— the Gathorne-Hardys of Great Glemham, Suffolk.

B. & H. 16895

This opera is the final section of the entertainment for young people called "Let's Make an Opera!" The first section of this is in the form of a play and illustrates the preparation and rehearsal of an Opera. It will be easily seen that professionals or very gifted amateurs are needed to play the grown-up parts and also the part of Juliet (provided, of course, that she can look convincingly youthful). It is essential that real children should play the children's parts—the boys with unbroken voices who shouldn't be scared of using their chest voices.

The accompaniment is for solo string quartet, piano-duet (four hands on one piano) and percussion (one player can manage). In the vocal score it is all arranged for piano-duet with or without percussion. (The piano-duet part printed here is not the same as that in the full version mentioned above, although the percussion part *is* the same). This reduced version can be used for actual performance but the original full version should be used where possible. The string parts are not very easy.

The songs, Nos. I, IX, XIV and XVII of the vocal score are to be sung by the whole audience under the direction of the conductor. They must, of course, be rehearsed beforehand. Allowance is made for such rehearsal in Part One of "Let's Make an Opera!"*

If only "The Little Sweep" is to be performed, the conductor will have to take a rehearsal with the audience and orchestra before the opera begins.

* *The libretto of "Let's Make an Opera!" can be obtained from the publishers of this score.*

The Characters of the Opera

Black Bob, *a brutal sweep-master* - - - - - - -	Bass
Clem, *his son and assistant* - - - - - - -	Tenor
Sam, *their new sweep boy, aged 8* - - - - - -	Treble
Miss Baggott, *the housekeeper at Iken Hall* - - -	Contralto
Juliet Brook, *aged 14* } - - - - - - - - -	Soprano
Gay Brook, *aged 13* } *the children of Iken Hall* -	Treble
Sophie Brook, *aged 10* } - - - - - - - - -	Soprano
Rowan, *the nursery-maid to the Woodbridge cousins* - -	Soprano
Jonny Crome, *aged 15* - - - - - - - -	Treble
Hugh Crome, *aged 8* - - - - - - - -	Treble
Tina Crome, *aged 8* - - - - - - - -	Soprano
*Tom, *the coachman from Woodbridge* - - - -	Bass
*Alfred, *the gardener at Iken Hall* - - - - - -	Tenor

** These two parts are doubled with Black Bob and Clem*

The action of the opera takes place in the children's nursery of Iken Hall, Suffolk, in the year 1810. The room is large and gaily-decorated and has two doors, a window and a fireplace. There is a toy-cupboard at one side of the fireplace, an armchair and a rocking-horse. The room is swathed in dust-sheets at the beginning of Scene One, but these are cleared away before Scene Two.

Scene One - - -	*A January morning.*
Scene Two - - -	*Later.*
Scene Three - - -	*The next morning.*

The first performances of "Let's Make An Opera!" were given at the Jubilee Hall, Aldeburgh (Suffolk) in June, 1949, as part of the second Aldeburgh Festival of Music and the Arts. Further performances were given during 1949 at the Wolverhampton and Cheltenham Festivals of Music, and at the Lyric Theatre, Hammersmith, during November, December, 1949 and January 1950. The entertainment was first broadcast in September, 1949, and televised in February, 1950.

The casts of these performances were:

Black Bob	*Norman Lumsden*	*John Highcock*
Clem	*Max Worthley*	*Andrew Gold*
Sam	*John Moules*	*Alan Woolston*
Miss Baggott	*Gladys Parr*	*Anne Wood*
Juliet Brook	*Anne Sharp*	
Gay Brook	*Bruce Hines*	*Michael Nicholls*
Sophie Brook	*Monica Garrod*	*Jean Galton*
Rowan	*Elizabeth Parry*	*Pamela Woolmore*
Jonny Crome	*Peter Cousins*	*Brian Cole* / *Paul Medland*
Hugh Crome	*Ralph Canham*	*Clive Wyatt*
Tina Crome	*Mavis Gardiner*	*Shirley Eaton*

Conductors: *Norman del Mar - Trevor Harvey*

Producers: *Basil Coleman and Stuart Burge*

Scenery and Costumes designed by John Lewis

Index

THE LITTLE SWEEP

I. THE SWEEP'S SONG

Words by
ERIC CROZIER

Audience Song I
later Clem, Bob

BENJAMIN BRITTEN
Op. 45

Printed in England

Aud.
brushes and scrapers and baskets and sacks To harvest the soot from our chim-er-ney stacks. So
I
II
Perc.
Aud.
Sweep! ....
Sweep! ....
meno f
Black Bob is coming and with him his lad, A
loco
meno f
ff
sf
mf

Aud.
sul-len ap-pren-tice as black as his Dad; Their cries as they ride through the sharp morning air Set
I
II
Perc.
2
dim.
partridges drumming and startle the hare. So Sweep!......... Sweep!.........
dim.
p
dim.
p
p
dim.

Aud.
Sam is the white boy, and sweep is his job, His fa-ther has-sold him to cru-el Black Bob. To-
I
II
Perc.
Aud.
-day is his black day: to-day he must climb A chim-er-ney stack for the ve-ry first time. So
cresc.
I
II
Perc.
cresc.

3
Aud.
Sweep! ....
Sweep! ....
f
Snape lies behind them, and ov-er the bridge They
I
II
Perc.
mf
strike to the left by a narrow-ing ridge; Then
fol-low the wan-der-ing dyke where it leads Through

4 CURTAIN
The nursery of Iken Hall
Aud.
thic-kets of rush-es and tus-socks of reeds. So - Sweep!
I
II
Perc.
Aud.
Sweep! (Tacet)
Enter Clem and Bob singing gaily, driving a miserable and tear-stained Sam before them.
CLEM
Sad-dle your don-key and set on your way! There's
BOB
Sad-dle your don-key and set on your way! There's
pp legatiss.

B. & H. 16895

Clem
chimneys need sweeping at I - ken to - day. Bring
brush-es and scrapers and baskets and sacks To
Bob
chimneys need sweeping at I - ken to - day. Bring
brush-es and scrapers and baskets and sacks To
I
II
Perc.
5
Clem
har-vest the soot from our chim - er - ney stacks. So
cresc.
Sweep!
Bob
har-vest the soot from our chim - er - ney stacks. So
cresc.
Sweep!
cresc.
sf
6
6
cresc.
Perc.

Clem
Sweep!
Sweep!
Bob
Sweep!
Sweep!
I
sf
f cresc.
II
6
6
f cresc.
Perc.
mf cresc.
Clem
Bob
I
ff
sf
II
ff
sf
Perc.
Cym. ffz
f
sec.

Attacca

II. QUARTET

Rowan, Miss Baggott, Clem and Bob

Miss B.
gap - ing! Four more chim-neys on this floor, Four more chim-neys on this floor, Four more
I
p
II
p
Miss B.
chim-neys, Four! Four! Give them all a thorough, all a thorough scra -
f
legato
f
marc.
6
ROWAN (tenderly. To Sam)
p
Small and white and stained with tears, with
Miss B.
- ping, scra-ping!
8
f
pp
f
p legato
sim.
(con Ped.)

R.
tears, Wrapped in scare - crow rags and pat - ches, in..... scare - crow rags and pat - ches, Faint
8
I
II
(sempre con Ped.)
R.
...... with ter - ror, full of fears, Wret - ched child
cresc.
p
cresc.
cresc.

* The small notes of the 2nd Piano, l.h., are to be played only if no percussion is available.

Clem
Bob
I
II
Perc.
cresc.
ferrets. Brush - es, rods and such-like toys .... Can't com -
- pete with hu - man me - rits. ....
dim.
mf cresc.
mf
p
ff
mf

8
ROWAN (as before)
f appassionato
Torn from play and sold for pay,.... for pay,.... Taught a
Miss BAGGOTT (as before)
f
Fil - thy ras - cals, fil - thy ras - cals, don't you dare, don't you dare Spread your
f (as before)
Clem
Choose 'em nim - ble, spry and thin—
f (as before)
Bob
Choose 'em nim - ble, spry and thin—
I
f
(mf)
II
f
Perc.
mf

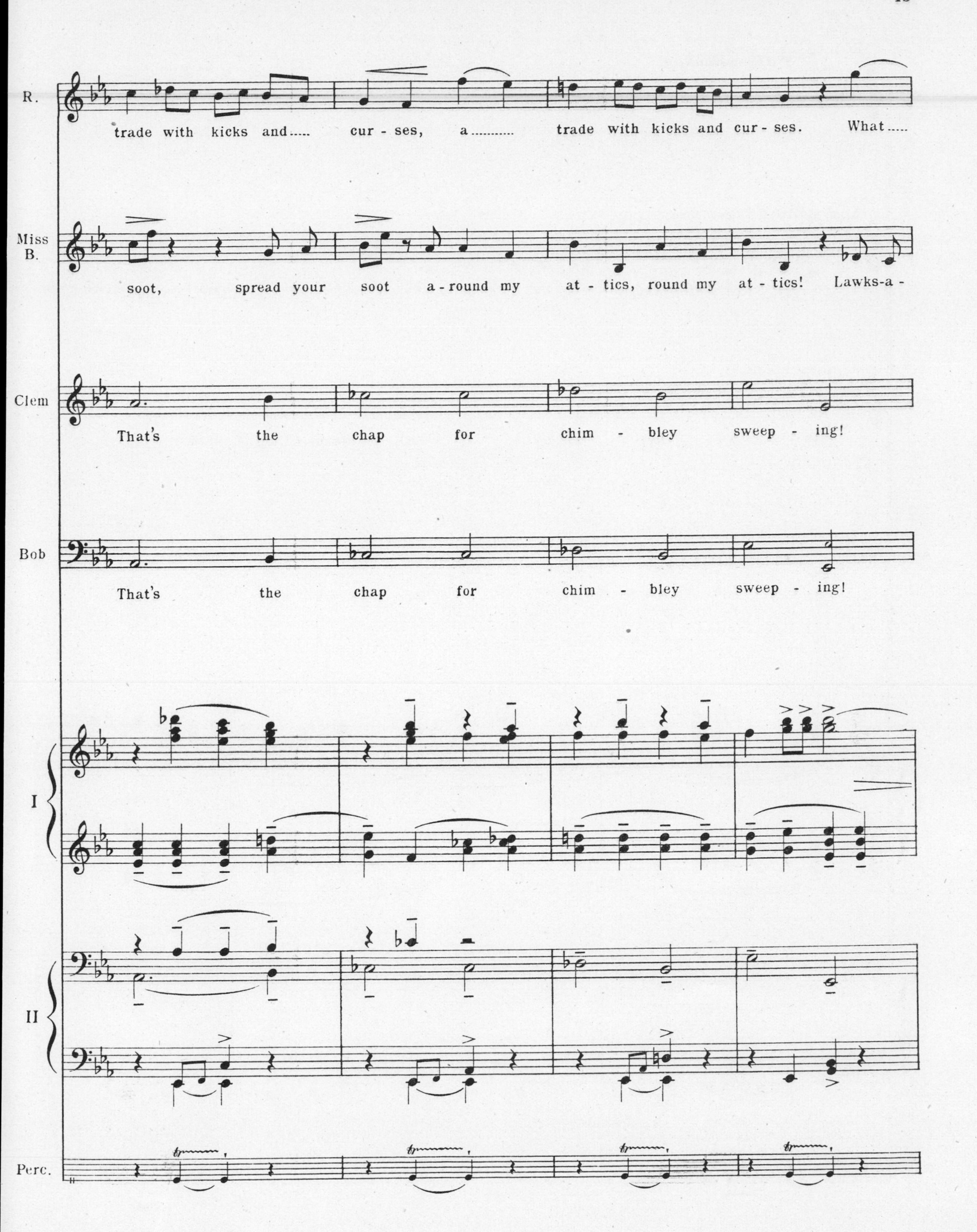
R.
trade with kicks and..... cur - ses, a........... trade with kicks and cur - ses. What.....
Miss B.
soot, spread your soot a - round my at - tics, round my at - tics! Lawks-a -
Clem
That's the chap for chim - bley sweep - ing!
Bob
That's the chap for chim - bley sweep - ing!
I
II
Perc.
tr
tr
tr
tr

R.
cresc.
...... can he.... do but o - bey.... Meek - ly.......
Miss B.
cresc.
- mer - cy, I de - clare, lawks - a - mer - cy I de - clare, I de - clare, Sweeps! Sweeps! Sweeps are
Clem
Ea - sy, too, for break - ing in,..................
Bob
Ea - sy, too, for break ing in,..................
I
sim.
cresc.
legato
II
cresc.
Perc.
tr
cresc.

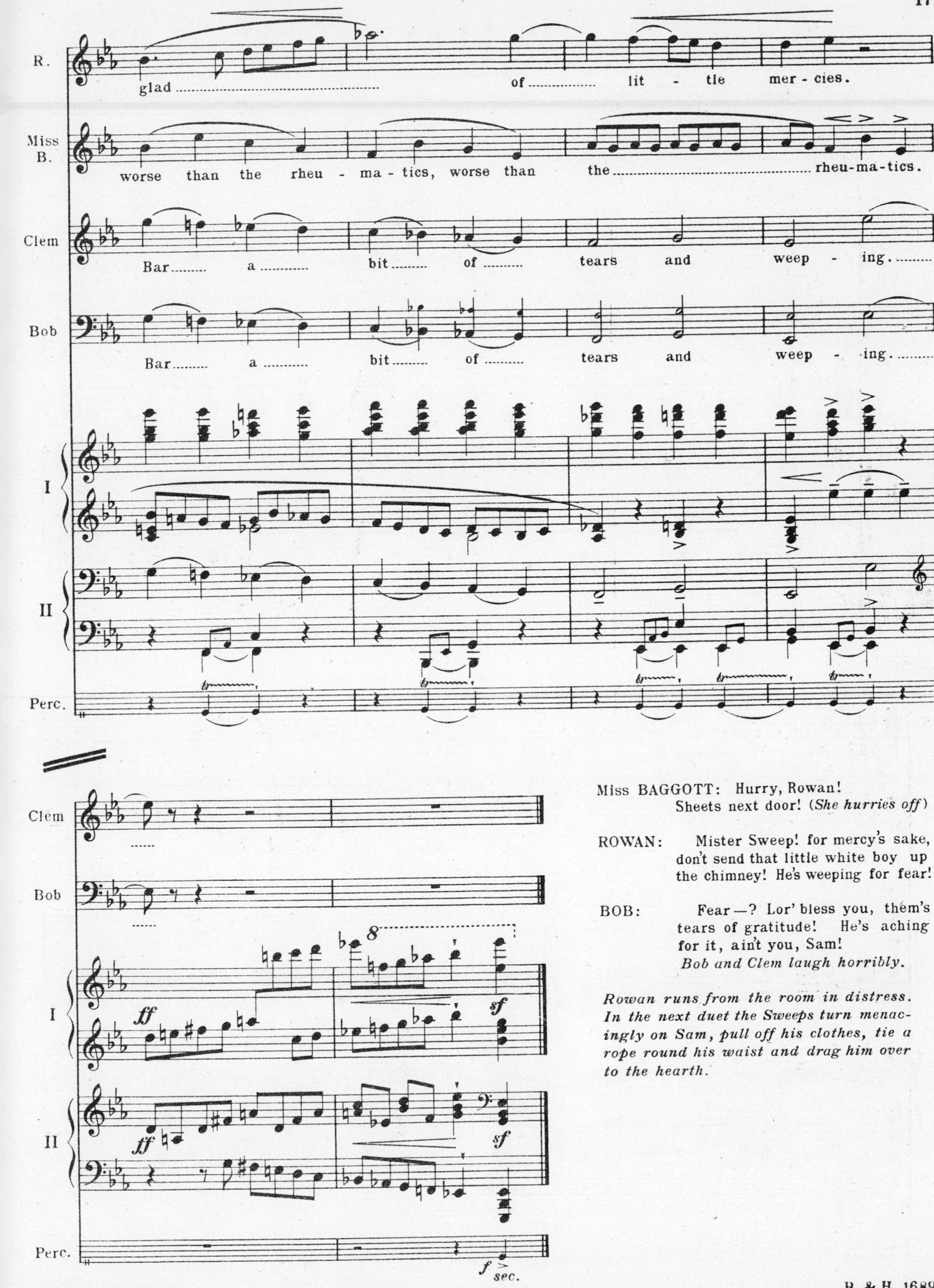

Miss BAGGOTT: Hurry, Rowan! Sheets next door! (*She hurries off*)

ROWAN: Mister Sweep! for mercy's sake, don't send that little white boy up the chimney! He's weeping for fear!

BOB: Fear—? Lor' bless you, them's tears of gratitude! He's aching for it, ain't you, Sam!
Bob and Clem laugh horribly.

Rowan runs from the room in distress. In the next duet the Sweeps turn menacingly on Sam, pull off his clothes, tie a rope round his waist and drag him over to the hearth.

III. DUET

Clem and Bob

*) Throughout this number, grace notes and glissandos are only to be played if there is no percussion.

9
Clem
Time for your climb!
Bob
Time for your climb!
8
white keys gliss.
I
II
Perc.
Clem
Don't kick or fight, boy!
Bob
Clothes off! my bright boy!
I
cresc.
II
cresc.
Perc.
cresc.

Clem
Time for your
Bob
piùf
Oh! so you'd bite, boy?
Time for your
I
II
Perc.
10
Clem
f
climb!
Bob
f
climb!
Pull the rope tight, boy!
p
white keys gliss.
ffz
mf
sf

Clem
piu f
Kiss us good - night, boy!
Bob
mf
Pull the rope tight, boy!
I
mf
II
mf
Perc.
p
Clem
Climb out of sight, boy!
f
Time for your
Bob
f
Time for your
I
cresc.
II
cresc.
Perc.

*) The small notes are to be played only if no percussion is available.

Clem
Bob
I
II
Perc.
dim.
Scra-per-and-sack boy!
A chim - bley stack boy!
dim.
Crawl-through-a-crack boy!
A
poco a poco dim.
poco a poco dim.
sim.
poco a poco dim.
A chim - bley, chim - bley, chim - bley, chim - bley
chim - bley stack boy!
A chim - bley, chim - bley

Clem
pp
ppp solenne
They laugh.
stack boy! Co - vered with grime!
Bob
pp
stack boy! Co - vered with grime!
I
solenne
pp
ppp
white keys gliss.
ffz
II
solenne
pp
ppp
ffz
Perc.
Gong
pp
S.D.
ppp
ffz
a tempo animato
The Sweeps collect their tools and march off into the next room.
12
ff
dim.
ff
dim.
Perc.
f
dim.

B.& H. 16895

*) The bass tremolandos only if no percussion.

IIIa. HIDE AND SEEK

CHILDREN *off stage*

(The door opens gently. Juliet slips in, shuts it carefully behind her and crosses to an armchair covered with a dust sheet.)

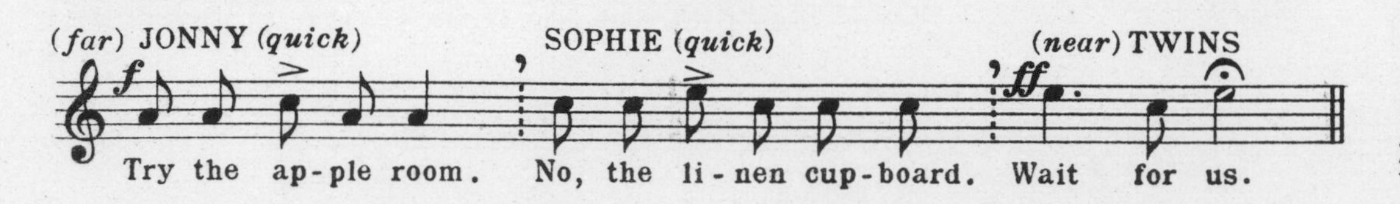

(Juliet slips into the chair beneath the sheet. The door flies suddenly open and the Twins pop their heads in.)

TWINS (*speaking*)
She's not in here!

(Juliet pokes her head above the sheet, emerges and approaches the door. It begins slowly to open.)

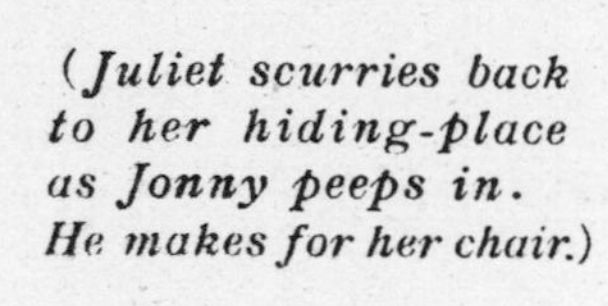
(Juliet scurries back to her hiding-place as Jonny peeps in. He makes for her chair.)

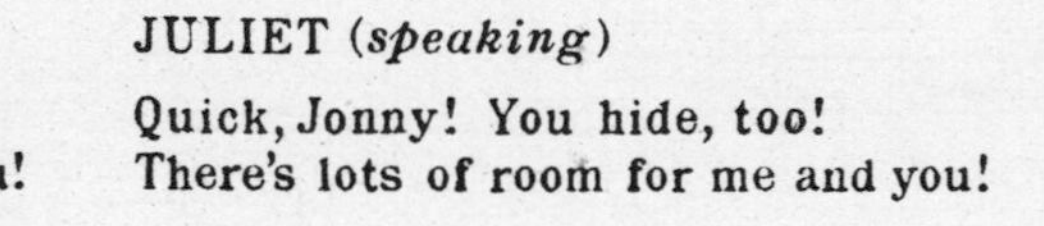
JONNY (*speaking*)
Caught you!

JULIET (*speaking*)
Quick, Jonny! You hide, too!
There's lots of room for me and you!

(They both hide in the chair with the sheet over them.)

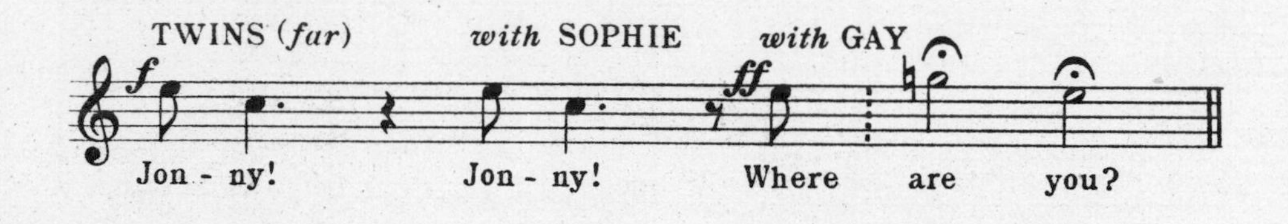

(Giggles from underneath the sheet. Suddenly the rope in the fireplace begins to waggle violently.)

SAM (*crying, off*)
Help! Help! I'm stuck!

JONNY, JULIET: (*showing themselves*)
What's that?

SAM: (*off*)
Pull me down!

JULIET:
It's a sweep boy!

JONNY:
In the flue!

SAM: (*off*)
Help! Help!

JULIET:
Call the others quickly, Jon!

CHILDREN: (*bursting into the nursery*) Here we are! What's going on?
JULIET: } JONNY: } Ssssh!
SAM: (*from the chimney*) Help! I'm suffocating!
JULIET: Pull him down!
JONNY: It's no good waiting!
(*All the children move to the fireplace.*)
JULIET: (*calls up the chimney.*) Hold very tight, and don't let go!
We'll pull the rope from down below!
(*The children pick up the rope, ready to pull.*)
BOYS: Ready?
SAM: (*from the chimney*) Ready!
JULIET: Pull as gently as you can.
We mustn't hurt the poor wee man!

IV. SHANTY

Children

Girls
Boys
I
II
Perc.
Pull O!
Heave O!
Pull the rope gent-ly un-til he is free.... O
(p)
(p)
p
pull!
Pull O!
Pull the rope gent-ly un-til he is free.... O
pull!
Heave O!

Girls
Pull O!
Pull O! Heave O!
Boys
Heave O!
Pull O! Heave O!
SAM: (from the chimney) No good!
JULIET: Pull harder this time—but not too hard!
I
II
Perc.
14
Girls
p
Pull the rope hard-er and give a good heave, O
p
p
pp

Girls
pull!
Pull O!
BOYS
p
Pull the rope hard-er and give a good heave O
pull!
Strong - ly O!
I
II
Perc.
Girls
cresc.
Pull O!
Pull the rope hard-er and give a good heave O
Boys
Strong - ly O!
cresc.
cresc.
poco cresc.

Girls
Boys
I
II
Perc.
cresc.
pull!
Pull O!
Pull the rope har-der and give a good heave O pull!
Strong - ly O!
Pull O!
Pull O!
Strong - ly O!
Strong - ly O!
Pull O!
Strong - ly O!
più f
più f
p
poco
SAM: (off)
I'm still stuck!
JULIET:
Try once more!

B. & H. 16895

15 Più animato
Girls
Pull the rope smart-ly with one two three jerk!
I
II
Perc.
Girls
One two three jerk!
BOYS
Pull the rope smartly with one two three jerk!
One two three jerk!
I
II
Perc.

(*With a loud scream Sam falls down the chimney and lies flat in the hearth.*)

CHILDREN:
Ooooohh!

TWINS & SOPHIE:
You've killed him!

(*The Children anxiously surround Sam and lift him up.*)

B. & H. 16895

V. ENSEMBLE

Sam and Children

Ch.
Sam
I
II
mf JULIET
Will Miss Bag - gott
p
Please don't send me up a - gain!
pp
p
sf
ff
mf
f JONNY
f with SOPHIE
f with JULIET
17
p TWINS
let us keep him? No she won't! No....... she won't! We'd ask in vain. She'd be-tray him
pp
mf with GAY
to his mas-ter, She'd be-tray him to his mas - ter.
SAM
Please don't send me up a - gain!
cresc.

JULIET
Ch.
Can't we res-cue him from sweeping?
Sam
Please don't send me up a-gain!
I
dim.
II
dim.
18
SOPHIE, JONNY
Hide him safe? And not ex-plain
TWINS
Till the sweeps have gone and left him,
cresc.
with GAY
Till the sweeps have gone and left him?
ALL
We won't send you up a-gain!

cresc.
Ch.
We won't send you up a - gain!
SAM
Please don't send me up a - gain!
I
cresc.
pp
II
cresc.
pp
p
ALL
Ch.
We won't send you up a - gain!
GAY (at the toy-cupboard.)
Hide him here, among our toys.
I
II
JONNY:
Room enough for twenty boys!
THE OTHERS:
Quickly, then!
JULIET:
But wait! I say! They must think he's run away!
SOPHIE:
Through the window!
TWINS:
Down the creeper!
ALL.
Come on, little chimney-sweeper!
I
II
Attacca

VI. MARCHING SONG

Children; later Miss Baggott, Bob, Clem

Vivace

The children lead Sam across the room, planting his feet to make tracks on the sheets.

19
Ch.
Clamber up and smudge the brick! Just a lit - tle not too thick! There's our dis - ap-pear-ing trick!
mf
I
mf
II
Perc.
poco accel.
20
Più presto
Someone's com-ing, someone's com-ing! Hide him! Hide him! Quick!
cresc.
f cresc.
ff
Cym.

The boys carry Sam to the toy-cupboard, snatch up his clothes, and dive under the shrouded furniture with
I
sempre f
II
sempre f
Perc.
B.D.
mf
the other children as
I
II
Perc.
Miss Baggott enters, followed by Clem and
Bob, with Rowan behind them.
I
ffz
II
ffz
ff
p
Perc.
sec.
Cym.
f
Miss BAGGOTT:
Half-past eleven! Hurry,
you idlers! Attics next!
BOB:
Yaps just like a little
old fox-terrier!
CLEM:
Real old blunderbuss,
ain't she?
Miss BAGGOTT:
What's this? Window open?

B. & H. 16895

Più lento
Miss BAGGOTT (all observing the marks of Sam's disappearance)
pp
Soot - y tracks up - on the sheet...
CLEM
Soot - y tracks up - on the sheet...
BOB
Soot - y tracks up - on the sheet...
II
ff
p
Cym.
Perc.
f
Miss B.
cresc.
lunga
Soot up - on the win - dow seat... Soot - y rope and
Clem
Soot up - on the win - dow seat... Soot - y rope and
Bob
Soot up - on the win - dow seat... Soot - y rope and
cresc.
Cym. f
accel.
soot - y noose .... Af - ter him! af - ter him! Young Sam - my's
mf cresc.
Attacca subito

VII. TRIO

Miss Baggott, Clem, Bob

*) Throughout this number the small notes in the 2nd Piano are only to be played if there is no Percussion.

Miss B.
teach him to run off and leave his du - ty!
Clem
teach him to run off and leave his du - ty, du - ty!
Bob
teach him to run off and leave his du - ty, du - ty!
I
II
Perc.
Miss B.
Chain him up and ken-nel him, Keep him with the fowls! And mor - ti - fy his pride, the lit - tle
Clem
Chain him up and ken-nel him, Keep him with the fowls! And mor - ti - fy his pride, the lit - tle
Bob
Chain him up and ken-nel him, Keep him with the fowls! And mor - ti - fy his pride, the lit - tle
f
mf
fp

Miss B.
beau-ty!
Lit-tle, lit-tle beau-ty!
lit-tle, lit-tle
Clem
beau-ty, beau-ty!
beau-ty!
Bob
beau-ty,
beau-ty!
beau-ty!
I
II
Perc.
fp
fp
Miss B.
beau - ty!
lit-tle, lit-tle, lit-tle, lit-tle, lit-tle, lit-tle,
Clem
beau - ty!
lit-tle, lit-tle, lit-tle, lit-tle,
Bob
beau - ty!
lit-tle, lit-tle,
I
II
Perc.
fp
fp cresc.

22
Miss B.
lit-tle, lit-tle, lit-tle, lit-tle beau - ty!
Clem
lit-tle, lit-tle, lit-tle, lit-tle beau - ty!
Bob
lit-tle, lit-tle, lit-tle, lit-tle beau - ty!
I'll give him
I
II
Perc.
f sempre
f sempre (non troppo f)
The Sweeps run off shouting furiously. Miss Baggott follows, calling them back.
Come back!
Li - ly - liv-ered toad!
'run a - way'!
I'll keel -

Miss B.
Come back!
Come back!
Clem
ff
Tar and fea-ther him!
Bob
- haul 'im round Snape Bridge!
I
dim. poco a poco
II
dim. poco a poco
Perc.
dim. poco a poco
23
Miss B.
Come back,
Come back you blackguards! six more chimneys, six more
Clem
Ah!
Bob
Ah!
I
(sempre con forza)
II
Perc.

(dying away)
Miss B.
chim-neys!
Come back!
come back!
come back!
I
pp
II
pp
Perc.
pp
Miss B.
come back!
poco rit.
I
ppp
poco rit.
II
ppp
molto
Perc.
molto
Attacca subito

*) During this number the 2nd Piano plays only if there is no percussion.

rall.
R.
e-choes make Sam shi-ver, Fill his heart with new des-pair.
I
pppp
Tria.
Perc.
25
molto stringendo
cresc.
Run, poor boy! O do not slacken, do not slacken! Black Bob follows swift, follows swift be-
pp
cresc.
Più presto
f
-hind! See his ang-ry fea-tures black-en! Rage and fu-ry
mf
poco a poco rilassando
make him blind!
ff
p

26
R.
p
How I wish that I could save you! I would hide you far a-
I
dim.
p
con Ped.
Perc.
Cym. ppp
R.
cresc.
-way From those tyr-ants who en-slave you And tor-ment you day by
l.h.
I
cresc.
Perc
poco cresc.
R.
appas. e sempre più f
day! How I wish that I could save you! How I wish that I could save you! How I
sim.
f
I
cresc.
Perc.
p

27
During the last verse the children's heads emerge from under their coverings, unnoticed by Rowan, and they watch her in admiration. She sees them suddenly. They stand up one by one, and beam at her.
R.
wish... ah!
CHILDREN
JONNY
Dear Ro-wan!
SOPHIE
cresc.
Dear, dear Ro-wan!
JULIET
Dea - rest
I
Perc.
Tria.
Ch.
GAY
più f
Ro-wan! Dea - rest, dar-ling Ro-wan!
TWINS
Dear, dea-rest, dar - ling-est
The children go to the cupboard door and beckon. Sam pokes out a timid and very sooty head.
ROWAN
What does this mean?
Twins
Ro-wan!
ALL CHILDREN
Sssh!
legatiss. quasi tremolando
ad lib.
2 Ped.

Rowan. Goodness gracious me! The Little Sweep!

Children. OUR Little Sweep!

Rowan. But whatever will Miss Baggott say to him?

Gay. She doesn't know . . .

Jonny. She needn't know . . .

Juliet. And she's *not* to know!

Twins. He's a Secret!

Rowan. But what are you going to do with him?

Twins. Feed him . . .!

Sophie. The poor boy's hungry.

Juliet. You see, Rowan, we can't possibly hand him over to those horrible sweeps, can we . . .?

[*Rowan hesitates, so the children answer for her.*]

Children. No—!

Juliet. . . . we can't possibly tell mama, 'cos she's away . . .

Gay. Seeing papa off to join his ship!

Juliet. . . . we can't possibly tell Miss Baggott . . .

Twins. 'Cos she'd turn him out of the house!

Juliet. . . . so you are the only grown-up we can tell!

Rowan. That's all very well for you, Miss Juliet, and for Master Gay and Miss Sophie, I daresay, but you must remember that your cousins and I are only visitors in your house . . .

Juliet. [*interrupting*]. Never mind about cousins and visitors! This is our latest visitor, and when you have a visitor who is cold and hungry and covered with soot from top to toe, what do you do with him . . .?

Twins. BATH him—!

Gay. Of course you do!

Sophie. But what about Miss Baggott?

Jonny. Oh, bother Miss Baggott!

Rowan. You need not worry for a little. I saw her crossing the courtyard in her clogs.

Jonny. Hooray! She's following the sweeps!

Gay. That gives us an hour to play with . . .

Rowan. I'm sure I don't know if you are doing right, Miss Juliet . . .

Juliet [*firmly*]. Look at him!—*Does* he need a bath, or doesn't he?

Children. *Yes*!

Rowan. Would you like to have a bath, Sammy?

Sam. Yes, please, Miss!

Juliet. Then you go and fill the buckets, Rowan . . .

Rowan. There's warm water on the hob . . .

Twins. We'll fetch the bath from the attic . . .!

Sophie. I'll get some clothes from Jonny's box . . .!

Jonny. I'll carry water . . .!

Gay. I'll light the fire . . .!

Juliet. I'll fetch soap and towels . . .! Is that all clear?

All. *Yes*!

Juliet. Then you stay in your cupboard, Sammy, and in five minutes we'll all be back for the Grand Transformation Scene!

All. *Come on*—!

[*The children scatter eagerly as the curtain falls.*]

END OF SCENE ONE

SCENE II

IX. SAMMY'S BATH

Audience Song II;
later Children, Rowan

Aud.
I
II
Perc.
sparks, The chil - dren...... run fly - ing...... To fetch what they're bid - den, For
bath: With brush - es.......... to scrub him,... With ba - sins to flood him, With
washing and dry - ing The sweep - boy.... they've hid - den. 2. They SPA -
flan - nels to rub him, With soap - balls to . . . . sud him.
1
2

Aud.
-LASH! in......... he plun-ges, And Ro-wan lets fly With sop - ping....
ff
I
II
Cym. (Timp. sticks)
Perc.
sf mf
Aud.
..... wet spon-ges And sparks in her eye! She wash - es.......... and
cresc.
I
II
Perc.
cresc.

Aud.
rin - ses........... And scrubs wil - ly - nil - ly, Till poor Sam - my
I
II
Perc.
tr
Aud.
win - ces But shines like........... a li - ly. And
f
I
II
f
Perc.
tr
dim.

28
Aud.
now Sam..... is gleam-ing Like snow in the sun, While Ro - wan stands
I
f
II
molto espr.
S.D.
sim.
Perc.
mf
Aud.
beam-ing To see her work done. So all who.... were frigh - tened When
I
II
8va bassa
Perc.

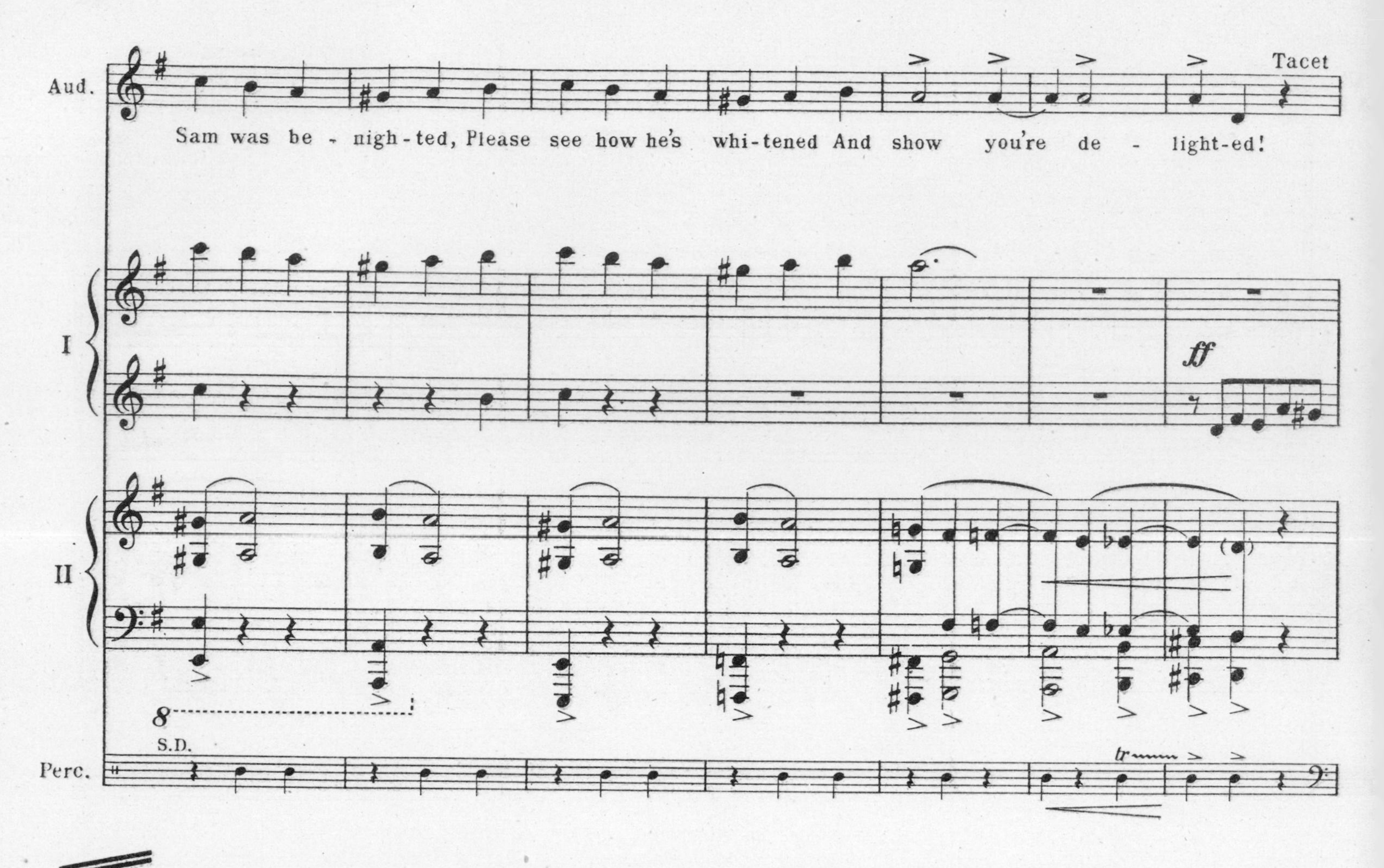

CURTAIN. *The nursery as before. The Children are watching the new Sam, as he finishes drying. Rowan is on her knees beside him.*

Ch. & R.
fly, O Sam - my...... is brigh-ter Than stars in the sky! O Sam is....
8
I
II
Perc.
Ch. & R.
..... as fair as The white - foam - ing seas, Or spin - drift....
8
I
II
Perc.

30
cresc.
Ch. & R.
...... in air, as Waves chal - lenge the breeze. The hate - ful.....
8
I
cresc.
II
cresc.
Perc.
ff
...... em - ploy - ment He suf - fered... so blind - ly...... Gives
ff
ff
f

Ch. & R.
way to en - joy-ment, gives way to en - joy-ment, gives way to en - joy-ment and
I
II
Perc.
Ch. & R.
thank....
SAM
Thank you all kind - ly!
I
II
Perc.

Rowan. Quick, children! We must tidy the room before Miss Baggott comes back.

Juliet. Just one moment, Rowan! Tell me, Sammy, haven't you any father or mother?

Sam. Yes, Miss.

Gay. Then where are they?

Sam. At home . . .

Jonny. Where's home?

Sam. Little Glemham.

Rowan. Little Glemham?—But I come from near Glemham myself! Whose boy are you?

Sam. Dad's name is Sparrow the waggoner.

Rowan. Josiah Sparrow, from along the ten-acre field?

Sam. That's him, Miss.

Juliet. And he sold you to that wicked sweep . . .?

Jonny. *Sold* you . . .?

Sophie. For money . . .?

Gay. Sold his own son . . .?

Twins. How *could* he . . .!

Sam. He didn't want to, but he broke his hip last threshing-time, and there wasn't anything to eat . . .

Rowan. Poor man!

Children. Poor Sammy!

Sam. But it's time I began work, they say. I shall be nine next birthday.

Children. [*shocked*] Only nine . . .!

[*The children are dismayed and unhappy to hear what Sammy has told them. They turn sadly to their task of tidying the room and help Sam into the clean clothes they have found for him.*]

X. ENSEMBLE

Sam, Rowan, Children

31
GAY & TWINS
pp
Fa-ther and
Sop.
weep at your task, poor boy?
ROWAN, SOPHIE, JULIET, JONNY
pp
Fa-ther and
I
pp
II
pp
SAM p
How shall I laugh and play?
Gay Twins
sf pp
mo-ther are far a-way.
R. Sop. Jul. Jon.
sf pp
mo-ther are far a - way.
I
p
II
sf pp p p

JONNY
p
O where is the home where your life .... was
I
II
pp
GAY
più f
O where is the home that you loved, poor boy?
Jon.
gay?
pp
p
più f

32
GAY & TWINS
Home is a hun-dred miles a - way.
ROWAN, SOPHIE, JULIET, JONNY
Home is a hun-dred miles a - way.
I
II
SAM
How shall I laugh and play?
Gay Twins
R.Sop. Jul.Jon.
I
II

TWINS
p
O
JULIET
f marc.
O what is that voice that you must o - bey?
8
(f)
dim.
I
II
f espress.
p
Twins
what is that voice that you fear, poor boy?
p
p

33
SAM
How shall I
GAY & TWINS
Mas - ter is an-gry a - gain to - day.
ROWAN, SOPHIE, JULIET, JONNY
Mas - ter is an-gry a - gain to - day.
I
II
Sam
laugh and play?
Gay Twins
R. Sop. Jul. Jon.
rall.

Jonny. I have an idea !

Juliet. What is it ?

Jonny. Rowan! when will you be packing our trunks ?

Rowan. Tonight, when you are in bed.

Jonny. Will you leave an empty space in the top of mine ?

Gay. I see ! Put Sammy in the trunk . . .

Juliet. And take him home with you !

Sophie. Oh, yes !

Twins. Hooray !

Rowan. But he'll stifle in a trunk . . . !

Gay. No, he won't.

Juliet. You can let him out as soon as you are clear of the house.

Rowan. I can't think what your father and mother will say to him.

Jonny. They'll help us, I'm positive they will !

Rowan. And where will you keep him for tonight ?

Gay. In the cupboard ! It's the only place.

Twins. [*at the window*]

Quick ! Quick ! She's coming !

Juliet. Who's coming ?

Twins. Miss Baggott !

Gay. Where ?

Sophie. Through the garden gate !

All. Hurry ! Hide Sammy ! Tidy the room !

[*The children are thrown into confusion by the unexpected return of Miss Baggott.*]

XI & XII. PANTOMIME AND SCENA

(Miss Baggott)

other with desperate haste to make the room look clean and tidy. Then they fetch books, toys and
I
II
Perc.
più
games with which to occupy themselves. Rowan takes a last quick look round the room, and settles
35
in the armchair with her knitting. The children form a sedate tableau around the fire. . . . . .

*) To be played only if no percussion is available.

*) The small notes to be played only if no percussion is available.

a tempo
ad lib.
f Adagio
pp
Miss B
Ah! Ah! The ver - min! All the way to Snape and back! Oh!.... my joints!
I
II
Perc.
pp
ff
(f)
subito
a tempo
38
ad lib.
Ne-ver! ne-ver! in all my born days... "Come back," says I, "come back," says I,
cresc.
fp colla parte
fp

a tempo
con forza
Miss B
"and fin-ish your law-ful work"
Their language! The in-sults! O drat, drat...
I
II
Perc.
pp
cresc.
*)
Miss B
(𝅗𝅥 = 𝅗𝅥)
f serioso
...... the sweeps!
For they .... that mock shall be a
ff
mf
il basso sempre ben marcato
f

*) as before

Miss B
nay - word and a by - word, and the good shall
I
più
p
II
più
p
poco dim.
Perc.
39
Allegro
Miss B
p cresc.
tram - ple them un - der - foot! The in - sults! The in - sults! Ac - cused
I
pp
II
pp
Timp.
Perc.
pp

*) as before

Miss B
me of hi-ding their beast - ly boy! I'll hide him! I'll hide him!
I
cresc.
II
cresc.
Perc.
cresc.
Miss B
I'll hide him! If once I lay my hands on him!
fff
ad lib.
pp
She sits.
lunga
f
ffz
f
ffz
ff

ad lib.
Miss B
Curtains crooked, Ro-wan! Care-lessness! Slap-dasher-y! Help me up!
I
II
The children assist her to rise, and she moves slowly around the room inspecting it.
Andante
Look at the crea - ses in the cur-tain!
sempre staccatiss.
sempre staccatiss.
Look at the foot-prints on the floor! You

Miss B
have - n't ti - died up, that's cer - tain:
Look at that fil - thy
I
II
cup - board door! Fire-place is grub - by, fen - der co - vered!
40
Bother Black Bob and both his boys!
Smudges of soot all round the cupboard!

She moves determinedly towards the toy-cupboard.
Miss B
Have you ar - ranged the chil - dren's toys?
I
II
f The children are on tiptoe with alarm.
Toys must be ti - died up com-plete-ly. Come o - ver here, you girls and boys!
cresc.
cresc.
8va basso
JULIET, collapsing dramatically
cresc.
O - pen the door and pack them neatly. Time that you ti - died up...... your toys!
ff
sf
ff
sf
8
Attacca subito

XIII. FINALE

Rowan, Miss Baggott, Children

Allegro

They surround the prostrate girl.

Miss BAGGOTT *f*

Help! help! she's collapsed! Help! help! she's collapsed! A fit of the vapours, the

I *ff* *f*

II *ff* *f* *)

Percussion { Cymbal / Bass Drum

Cym. *ff*

B.D. *mf*

ROWAN *espress. e legato*

Quick! Lift..... up her head! Rub her hands! Bring some

Miss B

va-pours! Help, help, she's collapsed! Help! help! she's collapsed! A fit of the vapours, the

I *f espr.*

II

Perc.

*) The grace notes of the 2nd Piano (l.h.) to be played only if there is no percussion.

R.
mf marc.
wa - ter! We'll put her to bed, we'll put her to bed, to bed! How
Miss B.
mf
va-pours! She's faint-ed! Stand back! She's faint-ed! Stand back! Stand back! Fetch feathers and
I
mf marc.
II
mf
Perc.
p
41
R.
luc-ky, how luc-ky you caught her!
Miss B.
f
ta - pers. Help! help! she's col -
CHILDREN (except Juliet) – kneeling reverently
p
Poor Ju-liet's ill!.................. Look how she's ly - ing, So
I
mf
II
p
Perc.
pp

R.
Miss B.
Ch.
I
II
Perc.
Quick, quick! Bring some
-lapsed!
Help! help! She's col - lapsed! Bring some
si - lent and still .... Can she be dy - ing?
wa - ter, bring some wa - ter, bring some wa - ter, wa - ter, quick, quick, quick!
wa - ter, bring some wa - ter, bring some wa - ter, wa - ter, quick, quick, quick!
Her

42
R.
quick, quick, quick! quick, quick, quick! Lift up her head, lift up her
Miss B.
quick, quick, quick! quick, quick, quick! Lift up her head,
Ch.
cheeks are so white pale a - la - bas - ter!
I
II
(p) cresc.
Perc.
pp
cresc.
R.
head, lift up her head, lift her head!
Miss B.
lift up her head! Rub her hands, rub her hands, rub her
I
II
Perc.
mf

43
R.
Rub her hands!
Rub her
Miss B.
hands, rub her hands!
Rub her hands!
CHILDREN
O dear, what a sight! What a di - sas - ter!
I
II
Perc.
R.
hands!
How luc - ky you caught her!
Lift up......... her
Miss B.
How luc - ky I caught her!
Help! help! she's col-lapsed! Help! help! she's col-
Ch.
Poor Ju - liet's ill!
staccatiss.
cresc.
cresc.

R.
cresc.
head,.... rub her hands, bring some wa-ter! We'll put her to bed, we'll
Miss B.
cresc.
-lapsed! A fit of the vapours, the va-pours! She's fain-ted, stand back! She's fain-ted, stand
Ch.
...... look how she's ly-ing! So si-lent and still .... can she be
I
f
cresc.
II
f
Perc.
R.
put her to bed! How luck-y, how luck - - y you caught her!
Miss B.
back! She's fainted, stand back, stand back! Fetch fea - thers and ta - pers!
Ch.
dy - ing? Dear, what a sight! .... What a di - sas - ter!
I
II
attacca subito
Perc.

Prestissimo
Rowan and Miss Baggott carry Juliet out, while the children dance round in a frenzy of excitement and relief.
CHILDREN
1. Blan - kets! Fea - thers! Warm - ing - pan!
2. Lift her legs! no, keep her flat!
ff martellato
martellato
S.D.
Perc.
Ch.
Run as quick - ly as you can! Bran - dy! Sal vo - la - ti - le!
A - ny sim - ple - ton knows that. Raise her head! Un - do her frock!

Ch.
Bar - ley wa - ter, Cups of tea!
Cold for fe - ver! Warmth for shock!
1
I
II
Perc.
2
Jonny runs to the cupboard, opens the door and calls to Sam.
JONNY
f largamente
Sit tight, Sam-my! and to-mor-row you're a free man!
mf
repeat ad lib.
pp

44
CHILDREN
ff
Ju - li - et has won the day In a ve - ry sim - ple way!
I
ff
II
ff
Perc.
mf
Ch.
f cresc.
Sam - my's safe and he can stay, Sam - my's safe and he can stay In his hi - ding
I
f cresc.
II
f cresc.
Perc.
p cresc.

Ch.
place, his hi - ding place, Hoo - ray! .... Hoo -
I
II
Perc.
ff
mf
senza rit.
The CURTAIN
closes on them.
- ray! .... Hoo - ray! ....
8
fff
f

XIV. THE NIGHT SONG

Audience Song III

Aud. I
Perc.
- hap - py cry: Tu - whoo! Tu - whoo! Tu - whoo! Tu -
p
pp
- whoo!
AUDIENCE (SECTION II - HERONS)
45
The he - ron lis - tens,

cresc.
Aud. II
gaunt and still, With - in his nest up - on the hill, Then parts a stern and
I
cresc.
II
cresc.
Perc.
Aud. II
(nasal)
f
sa - vage bill: Kaah! Kaah! Kaah!
I
f
II
f
Castanets
Perc.
mf
mf
mf

Aud. II
Kaah!
I
sim.
II
sim.
Perc.
mf
mf
dim.
AUDIENCE (SECTION III – DOVES)
46
p
The turtle dove begins to stir, Re-
dim.
p dolce
dim.
p sost.
pp Gong

Aud. III
- moves the leaves that shel - ter her, And ans - wers with me - lo - dious
I
II
Perc.
Aud. III
purr: Prrr - ooo!
Prrr - ooo!
Prrr - ooo!
I
II
Cym. susp.
p
Perc.

Aud.
III
Prrr - ooo!
I
9
9
cresc.
II
cresc.
Perc.
poco cresc.
47
AUDIENCE (SECTION IV – CHAFFINCHES)
p
The
tr
f
p
tr
f
p
Perc.
mf

ud. V
chaf - finch and his mate re - joice To ex - er - cise their sing - ing voice. They
I
II
Gong
pp
erc.
(falsetto)
Aud. IV
pp
take the des - cant for their choice: Pink! Pink! Pink! Pink! Pink! Pink!
I
pp
II
p
Tria. (hard stick)
pp
Perc.

Aud. IV
Pink! Pink! Pink!
Pink! Pink! Pink!
I
cresc.
II
cresc.
Perc.
cresc.
Cym. (hard stick)
AUDIENCE (ALL SECTIONS)
f
From
I
II
f
Perc.

48
North and South and East and West The birds com-pete for who sings best, But
f espress.
I
marc.
II
Perc.
mf Gong
Repeat this bar (sempre ff) until a sign from the conductor.
I
who shall choose the love - li - est? Tu- whoo! Tu-
II
who shall choose the love - li - est? Kaah! Kaah!
Aud.
III
who shall choose the love - li - est? Prrr-ooo! Prrr-ooo!
IV
who shall choose the love - li - est? Pink! Pink! Pink! Pink! Pink! Pink!
ff
B.D.
sempre f

I
Aud.
II
- whoo!
dim.
8
7
I
II
dim.
Perc.
tr
dim.
AUDIENCE (ALL SECTIONS)
pp
49
The night is past, the owl is hoarse, The
pp
Gong

Aud.
fin - ches slum - ber in the gorse, The he - ron stoops, the tur - tle
I
II
Perc.
Repeat this bar as before, dying away to nothing.
I
droops. Tu - whoo! Tu - whoo!
II
droops. Kaah! Kaah!
Aud.
III
droops. Prrr - ooo! Prrr - ooo!
IV
droops. Pink! Pink! Pink! Pink! Pink! Pink!
pp dim.
dim. sempre
pppp
pp
dim.
con Ped.
ppp dim.
dim. sempre
pppp

SCENE THREE

[The following morning. Rowan has just entered the nursery with a breakfast-tray for Juliet, who is wearing a warm quilted dressing-gown. She puts the tray down and they go to the cupboard to fetch Sammy.]

Dialogue

Rowan. Breakfast, Sammy !

Juliet. Ham and eggs !

Rowan. Stretch yourself—

Juliet. And kick your legs !

Rowan. Only twenty minutes more
Till the coach is at the door !

[Rowan hurries off again. Sam stretches himself.]

Juliet. Hungry, Sammy ?

Sammy. Oh yes, Miss !

Juliet. Eat away then, while I unstrap this trunk.

[Sam sits at the table and begins to eat. Juliet unstraps the trunk, singing.]

XV. ARIA

Juliet

50
Jul.
lit-tle sweep we res - cued yes - ter-day
I
f
mf
sim.
p
II
dim.
dolce
Set off a-long the road to li - ber-ty.
pp ritmico
p
con più forza
Black you were, you poor un-hap-py mite,
espress.
più tenebroso

51
Jul.
And ve - ry ug - ly too,
I
II
cresc.
f
(mf)
mf
... I must con-fess!
To - day you're
pp
gui - nea - bright ... and gleam - ing white,
And
p
poco cresc.

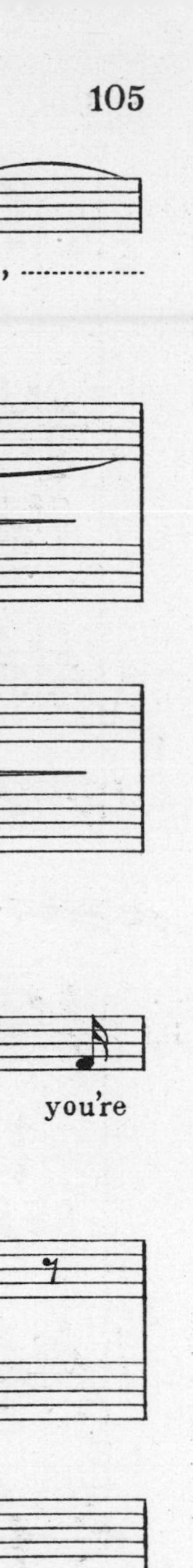

espress.
Jul.
ra - diant with joy and hap - pi - ness.
I
f espress.
II
f
52
Jul.
f
Sam - my dear, to -
espress.
I
f sonoro
II
f sonoro
Jul.
- day at last you are free!
p
Your cruel ap - pren - tice - ship
I
p
II
p

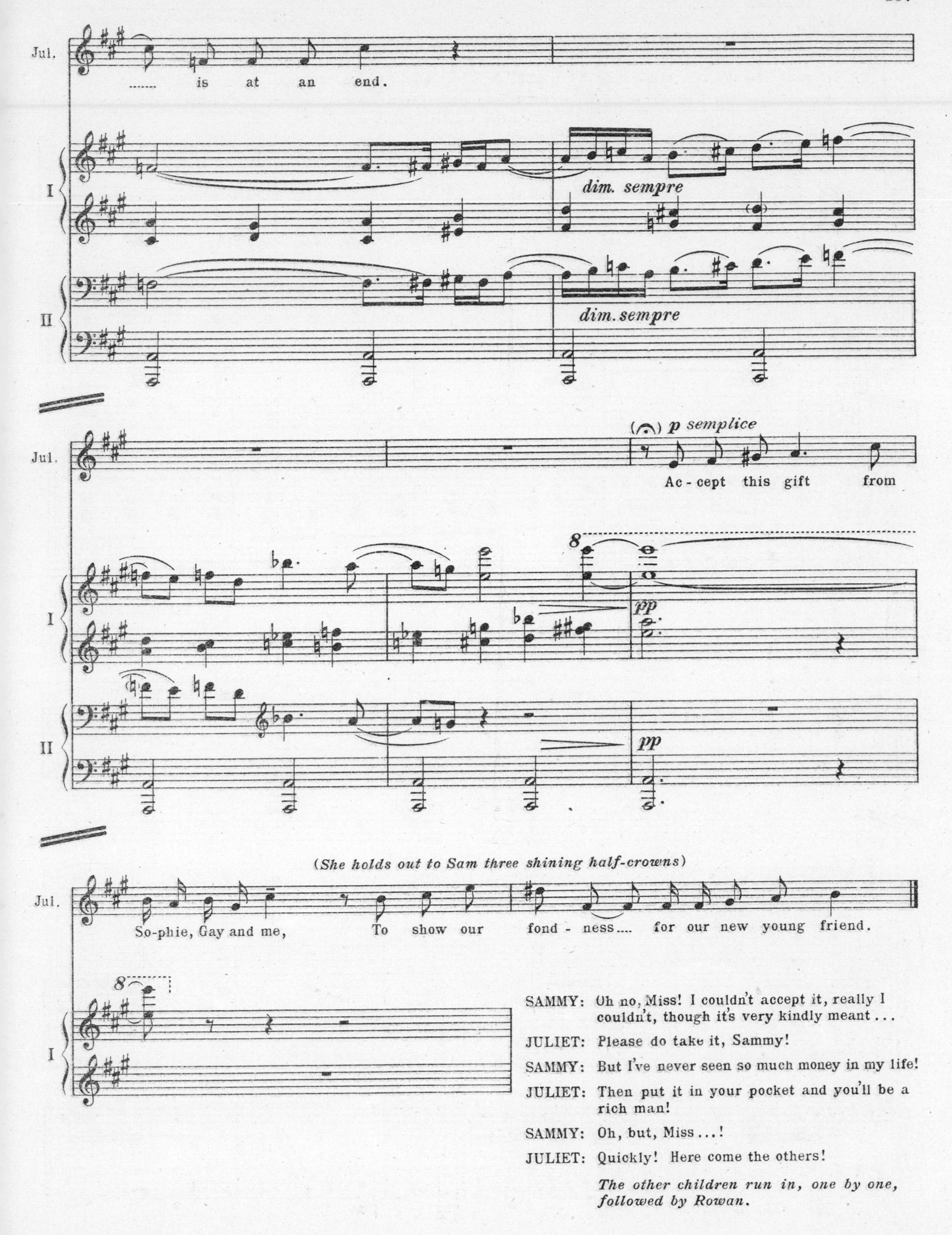

SAMMY: Oh no, Miss! I couldn't accept it, really I couldn't, though it's very kindly meant . . .

JULIET: Please do take it, Sammy!

SAMMY: But I've never seen so much money in my life!

JULIET: Then put it in your pocket and you'll be a rich man!

SAMMY: Oh, but, Miss . . . !

JULIET: Quickly! Here come the others!

The other children run in, one by one, followed by Rowan.

XVI. ENSEMBLE

Sam and Children

SOPHIE
f
'Morn - ing, Sam - my! You look splen-did Now your sweep-ing -
p
I
II
54
Enter Gay
Sop.
- days are end - ed!
SAM
'Morn - ing 'Morn - ing
sf
GAY
'Morn - ing, Sam - my! Time to tra - vel! I hear coach-wheels on the gra - vel!
mf

SAM
55
Enter the Twins
'Morn - ing! 'Morn - ing!
I
II
HUGHIE
'Morn - ing, Sam-my! We're de-ligh-ted .... that you're safe and so ex -
TINA
'Morn - ing, Sam-my! We're de - ligh - ted that you're safe and so ex -

HUGHIE & TINA
cresc.
with GAY
with SOPHIE
Ch.
-ci - ted! 'Morn - ing,
Sam - my! 'Morn - ing,
Sam - my! 'Morn - ing,
I
cresc.
II
cresc.
with JONNY
Sam - my! Morn - ing, Sam - my!
SAM (f)
'Morn - ing! 'Morn - ing!
ff
pp
p

Jonny. The coach is coming—

Gay. Into the trunk with you !

Rowan. I'll fetch your hats and coats.

[*She goes off quickly to get them.*]

Juliet. In you jump !

Gay. Take some bread and butter with you.

[*Sam gets into the trunk and kneels.*]

Juliet. Goodbye, Sammy dear, and very good luck !

[*She kisses him.*]

Sophie. Goodbye, dear Sammy ! [*She kisses him.*]

Gay. Jolly good luck to you, Sammy ! [*Handshake.*]

Rowan. [*returning with hats and coats*] Hurry, children ! The coach is at the door !

[*Juliet and Gay hastily strap up the trunk, while Sophie watches at the door, and Rowan helps Jonny and the Twins into their travelling clothes.*]

Sophie. Quickly! Quickly! Quickly! I can hear voices !

Gay. Finished !

Juliet. [*kneeling by the trunk*] Are you all right, Sammy ?

Sam. [*muffled, from inside*] Yes, thank you, Miss ! Very comfortable.

[*The children clap their hands in silent glee.*]

Miss Baggott. [*off*] Come along, the pair of you ! Mind the paint, or I'll know the reason why !

[*She enters the room followed by Tom, the coachman from Woodbridge, who is muffled up in an enormous overcoat, and by Alfred, the gardener, in apron and leggings. They are not a bit afraid of Miss Baggott.*]

Tom. Whoo ! Stairs took me wind away ! Whoo !

Alfred. Terrible old house for stairs, this.

Miss Baggott. That's the trunk and mind the corners !

Tom. Whoa, Missus, whoa ! Mustn't flog a willing horse ! Easy does it !

Alfred. Them stairs catch me a slap in my lumbago.

Miss Baggott. Come along, my men !

Tom. Gently, Ma, gently with the bearing rein !—How's that strong right arm of yours, Alfred lad ?

Alfred. It's the small of the back does me, Tom. The spirit's willing, but the small of the back says " Careful, Alfred, careful ! "

Tom. Shall we take a dab at that little old trunk ?

Alfred. No hurry, Tom. Whenever you're certain of your breath and suchlike.

Tom. Now, let's understand each other, Alfred boy. When I says *three* we lift, if you take my meaning. ' One — Two — Three,' and up she'll come like the morning lark.

XVII. TRIO AND ENSEMBLE

Clem, Bob, Miss Baggott; later Rowan and Children

56

Miss BAGGOTT *f*

Heave it up and off you go!

Alf. *f* Wait for me! *p* One and two and

Tom ...... and... *p* Sor-ry, Al-fred! One, two, three?

I *f* *p dolce* *p*

II *f* *p*

Cym.

Perc. *f* *p*

Miss B Hur-ry! Car-ry it be-low!

Alf. three and lift! What's in-side it?

Tom *p* No, the drat-ted thing won't shift! Full of

I *sim.*

II *sim.*

Perc.

Alf.
Twice as hea - vy as it looks.
Tom
books!
cresc.
Come a-long, we'll car-ry it be-low
I
II
cresc.
f
Perc.
cresc.
f
Miss BAGGOTT
f
What a stu-pid fuss to make A - bout a trunk!.... For good - ness' sake!
I
p dolce
II
Perc.

57
Miss B.
ALFRED
TOM
Can't you
Feels like screwed down to the floor. Weighs like lead, but twice as
Feels like screwed down to the floor. Full of stones, or sand or such!
I
II
sim.
Perc.
lift one lit-tle box Packed with shoes and shirts and socks?
Recit ad lib.
Alf.
much.
Tom
Can't be done, Mis-sus!
dim.

Play grace notes and tremolo marked *) in 2nd Piano, l.h. only if there is no percussion.

58
poco accel.
ALL CHILDREN
Oh, no!
Alf.
Or we leave her where she lies!
O,
con più forza
Tom
Ei - ther that there box is un - packed or we leave her where she lies!
O,
I
II
T.D.
S.D.
Perc.
ROWAN
f ad lib.
Mister Tom, we'll help you to lift the box!
Ch.
Oh, no!
Yes, please let us help!
yes!
O, yes!
B.D.
Cym.
sec.

Alf.
Ve - ry kind in-deed!
Tom
tranquillo
Well, that's a fair of-fer, Miss, and kind-ly meant. What's your view, Alfred?
II
All, except Miss Baggott gather round the trunk.
Vivace
ROWAN
Good!.... ev - 'ry - one help lift!
Tempo I
CHILDREN
Ev - 'ry-one help lift!
I
II
play in lieu of Bass Drum
Perc.
B.D.

With a concerted effort they help the men lift the trunk.
59
R.
One two and three, Up she comes Hip-hoo-
Ch.
One and two and three, hoo-ray! Up she comes Hip-hip-hoo-ray!
ALFRED
One two and three, Up she comes Hip-hip-hoo-
TOM
One two and three, Up.... she comes!
I
II
8ve bassa
Perc.
T.D.
S.D.
B.D.
poco f (Solo)

R.
cresc.
-ray!.........................
Ma - ny hands make la - bour light. Now you'll
Ch.
cresc.
Ma - ny hands make la - bour light.
Now you'll man - age
Alf.
cresc.
-ray! Hip - hip - hoo - ray!
Ma - ny hands make la - bour
Tom
cresc.
Hip - hip - hip - hip - hoo - ray!
Now
sim.
I
cresc.
II
cresc.
8
Perc.
cresc.

60
(The men go off carrying the trunk. Miss Baggott following).
R.
man - age her.... al - right.
Miss BAGGOTT
Mind the paint! Mind the paint! Don't drop it! Ea - sy round the cor-ners!
Ch.
her al - right.
Alf.
light, make la - bour light.
Tom
she's al - right.
I
dim.
II
dim.
sim.
Cym.
Perc.
dim.
dying away
Miss Baggott continues until inaudible...
Miss B
ea - sy round the corners, Don't drop it! Don't drop it! Don't drop it! Don't drop it! Don't drop it...
p sempre dim.
p sempre dim.
play tremolo in lieu of Bass Drum
p sempre dim.

XVIII. FINALE – COACHING SONG

Audience Song IV with stage

ROWAN & CHILDREN: (*spoken*)

He's gone, thank goodness, on his way.—And thank you for our holiday.— Goodbye, my dears, goodbye!

GAY, JULIET & SOPHIE:

Quick, open the window! Look! There's the trunk! They're lifting it into the coach! He's safe at last! Sammy's safe!

(*Jonny, Twins and Rowan hurry off*)

GAY, JULIET & SOPHIE:

There come the others! They're climbing into the coach. Goodbye, Jonny! Goodbye, Twins!

OTHERS (*off*) Goodbye, Goodbye!

GAY, JULIET & SOPHIE:
(pp) And goodbye, Sammy!
dear Sammy!

61

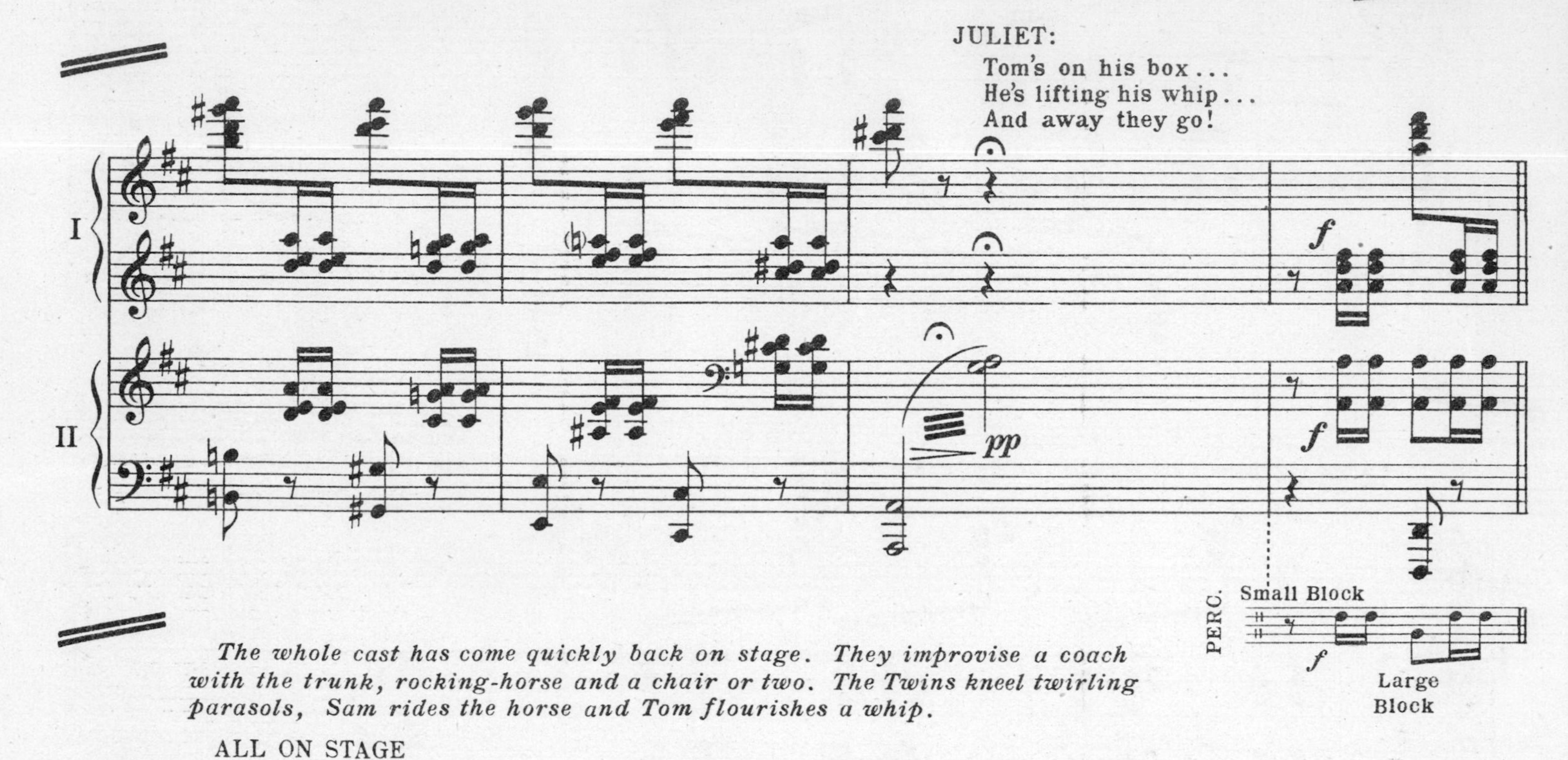

The whole cast has come quickly back on stage. They improvise a coach with the trunk, rocking-horse and a chair or two. The Twins kneel twirling parasols, Sam rides the horse and Tom flourishes a whip.

ALL ON STAGE

62
WITH AUDIENCE
All
coach - man lets slip!
way from our sight.
So there! So there! Good brown mare,
I
II
sempre f
Perc.
All
Lead a - way at a spank - ing trot.
1
2
spank - ing trot.
Perc.

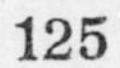

STAGE f
All
3. They swing from the by - road on to the high - road,
4. Now Sam has a - ri - sen out of his pri - son,
sempre f
I
II
Perc.
63
WITH AUDIENCE
Ga - ther - ing pace for the home a - gain race!
Grin - ning with glee to be hap - py and free!
Ho there! Ho there!

*) The R.H. chords of the 2nd Piano to be spread only if percussion is *not* available.

All
You who've at - tend - ed Join in the song as the coach runs a - long!
I
II
Perc.
64 WITH AUDIENCE
ff
All
Go there! Go there! Let me see you gal - lop! Gal - lop, gal - lop,
I
ff
II
ff
Perc.
ff

poco a poco rall.
ff
All
good brown mare! Whoa there! Whoa there!
I
II
Perc.
65
Sempre più lento
Slac - ken pace! Stea - dy now, you've won the race! Time to

LOWE AND BRYDONE PRINTERS LIMITED, LONDON

10

Benjamin Britten

OPERAS

Op. 33. Peter Grimes
Op. 37. The Rape of Lucretia
Op. 39. Albert Herring
Op. 43. The Beggar's Opera (*A New Realisation*)

ORCHESTRAL

Op. 1. †Sinfonietta *for Chamber Orchestra*
Op. 9. Soirées Musicales
Suite of 5 Movements from Rossini
Op. 10. Variations on a Theme of Frank Bridge
for String Orchestra
Op. 12. Mont Juic (with Lennox Berkeley)
Suite of 4 Catalan Dances
Op. 13. Piano Concerto (*Revised Version*)
Op. 15. Violin Concerto
Op. 19. Canadian Carnival (Kermesse Canadienne)
Op. 20. †Sinfonia da Requiem
Op. 21. Diversions *for Piano (Left Hand) and Orchestra*
Op. 24. Matinées Musicales
Second Suite of 5 Movements from Rossini
Op. 26. Scottish Ballad *for 2 Pianos and Orchestra*
Op. 29. Prelude and Fugue *for 18-part String Orchestra*
Op. 33a. †Four Sea Preludes from "Peter Grimes"
Op. 33b. †Passacaglia from "Peter Grimes"
Op. 34. †The Young Person's Guide to the Orchestra
Variations and Fugue on a Theme by Purcell

INSTRUMENTAL

Op. 2. †Phantasy
Quartet for Oboe, Violin, Viola and Cello
Op. 5. Holiday Diary *Suite for Piano*
Op. 6. Suite *for Violin and Piano*
Op. 23. No. 1. Introduction and Rondo Alla Burlesca
No. 2. Mazurka Elegiaca
each for 2 Pianos, 4 Hands
Op. 25. †String Quartet No. 1 in D
Op. 36. †String Quartet No. 2 in C

VOCAL

Op. 7. Friday Afternoons
12 Children's Songs with Piano (2 Vols.)
Op. 8. Our Hunting Fathers
Symphonic Cycle for High Voice and Orch.
Op. 11. On This Island (*5 Songs*)*
Op. 18. †Les Illuminations
for High Voice and String Orchestra
Op. 22. Seven Sonnets of Michelangelo
for Tenor and Piano
Op. 31. †Serenade *for Tenor, Horn and String Orchestra*
Op. 33. Three Arias from "Peter Grimes"
with Orchestra or Piano
Op. 35. The Holy Sonnets of John Donne
for Tenor and Piano
Op. 37. Three Arias from "The Rape of Lucretia"
with Orchestra or Piano
Op. 40. Canticle I (Francis Quarles)
for Tenor and Piano
Op. 41. A Charm of Lullabies
for Mezzo Soprano and Piano
The Birds *Song for Medium Voice*
Fish in the Unruffled Lakes*
Folk Songs, Vol. 1. British Isles**
Vol. 2. France** Vol. 3. British Isles**

CHORAL

Op. 14. Ballad of Heroes
for High Voice, Mixed Chorus and Orchestra
Op. 27. Hymn to St. Cecilia
for Unaccompanied Mixed Chorus
Op. 28. A Ceremony of Carols
for Treble Voices and Harp or Piano
Op. 30. Rejoice in the Lamb
Festival Cantata for Choir and Organ
Op. 32. Festival Te Deum *for Choir and Organ*
Op. 42. Saint Nicolas, *Cantata for Tenor Solo, Mixed Voices, String Orchestra, Piano and Percussion*
Hymn to the Virgin,
Unaccompanied Anthem for Mixed Double Chorus
I Lov'd a Lass,
Part Song for Mixed Voices and Piano
Advance Democracy, *Part Song for Mixed Voices*

HENRY PURCELL

Realisations by Benjamin Britten

The Golden Sonata *for 2 Violins, Cello and Piano*
Orpheus Britannicus :—
Seven Songs**
Six Songs**
Suite of Songs *for Tenor and Small Orchestra*
The Queen's Epicedium*
Harmonia Sacra :—
The Blessed Virgin's Expostulations*
Saul and the Witch at Endor
for Soprano, Tenor, Bass and Piano
Three Divine Hymns**

**For High Voice and Piano* ***For High or Medium Voice and Piano*

† Pocket Scores available *For Prices See Current Catalogue*

Boosey & Hawkes
Limited
295 Regent Street, London, W.1
New York · Los Angeles · Sydney · Capetown · Toronto · Paris

No. 512 10.48